Agent Blue and the Super-smelly Goo

AND

Agent Blue and the Swirly Whirly

BY DEBBIE WHITE

ILLUSTRATED BY REBECCA CLEMENTS

OXFORD
UNIVERSITY PRESS

Helping your child to read

Before they start

- Look at the back cover blurb. What kinds of adventures might a spy pigeon like Agent Blue have?

- Flick through the book together. Does your child like reading comic-style stories? Briefly share some ideas about what might happen in the stories.

During reading

- Let your child read at their own pace, either silently or out loud.

- If necessary, help them to work out words they don't know by saying each sound out loud and then blending them to say the word, e.g. *a-ss-i-s-t-a-n-t, assistant.*

- Encourage your child to keep checking that the text makes sense and they understand what they are reading. Remind them to reread to check the meaning if they're not sure.

- Give them lots of praise for good reading!

After reading

- Look at page 79 for some fun activities.

Agent Blue
AND
THE SUPER-SMELLY GOO

At the Pigeon Spy Agency, Stella Bird has bad news for her assistant, Perch. Birdseed, their greatest enemy, is advertising for strong pigeons. He's up to no good again ...

Blast! Birdseed is causing trouble again. We can't send an undercover agent. He's already met them all!

WANTED:
STRONG, FIT PIGEONS.
APPLY ONLINE. SEND A PHOTO.
BIRDSEED

Except for Blue, our new agent.

Minutes later, Blue is in Stella Bird's office.

Birdseed is planning something. We need you to go undercover and find out what. Do you think you can do it?

Yes, Chief!

Good. Get on with Blue's training, Perch.

Help! No time to lose.

First, Perch has to get Blue fit and strong so Birdseed will want to hire him.

I said loop the loop and THEN drop like a stone!

FOCUS, Agent Blue!

Tired? Give me 100 more press-ups!

Next, Blue is given new clothes and an undercover name.

BEFORE

My name is Pond … Max Pond!

AFTER

Then Blue uses his undercover name to reply to Birdseed's advertisement.

Hurry up and take the photo, Perch. My beak looks best from this side!

FLASH!

MAX POND

Name: Max Pond
Age: 8
Male/Female: Male
Place of Birth: Tree House, Dove Street
Interests: Karate and playing *Angry Pigeons*

Next comes the secret agent stuff, like how to crack secret codes.

Then Blue goes to see Professor Z. She gives him a spy watch that's also a computer AND a phone.

Professor Z fits a slip-and-slide spray under Blue's left wing …

… a lock-busting kit under his right wing …

… and turbo-charged rockets in his wing tips.

CLICK

These gadgets are made from the latest materials. They are as light as a feather and cannot be detected by security systems.

Professor Z also hides sleepy powder in Blue's spy watch.

Later Blue gets an email from Birdseed ...

Come and see me, Mr Pond.

My base. 8 p.m. sharp.
Map attached.

Birdseed

... and Blue is ready
to start his undercover
mission as Max Pond.

It's getting late when Blue arrives at a huge volcano. He looks for the entrance to Birdseed's base.

The lift shoots up and the doors open into a huge room full of pigeons.

A couple of pigeons stare as Blue walks past.

This is your perch, Mr Pond. Wait here for your instructions.

Blue secretly checks the phone on his spy watch.

Oh no! There's no signal in this volcano!

Blue leans across to talk to the pigeon on the next perch.

Do you know what's happening?

You'll find out soon!

Suddenly, Birdseed appears in the doorway.

Welcome, Max Pond ... or should I call you AGENT BLUE?

How do you know my real name, Birdseed?

Simple, Agent Blue. The camera at the security gate worked out who you were within minutes. Clever, eh?

But not as clever as my plan to ruin the Golden Feather Awards. I'm going to drop super-smelly goo on everyone!

Five years ago, Pigeon Pictures turned Birdseed down for a big acting job. He's been bitter ever since.

PIGEON
PICTURES
——
Auditions
TODAY

NOOOOOOOO!!!

Birdseed has the acting talent of a worm!

Rock will be watching you so don't even think about trying to escape. You're NOT going to spoil my plan!

Oh yes I am. I'll stop you!

At six o'clock the next morning …

BING! BING! BING!

The pigeons hop off their perches and head for the lift.

Blue wakes with a jolt and rushes towards the lift, too.

So that's why the lift is so big!

But Rock stops him in his tracks.

Only the Pigeon Squad goes upstairs for goo training – not spies!

Rock chains Blue to his perch.

I need to break free and come up with a different plan for tomorrow.

During the night, Blue uses his lock-busting kit to break the lock.

At six o'clock the next morning, Blue is ready.

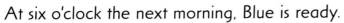

BING! BING! BING!

The Pigeon Squad goes up to Level 3.

2

1

3

Ping! Ping!

Time to use the sleepy powder on Rock.

SNORE

WHOMP!

Rock hits the ground snoring.

Blue whips out his slip-and-slide spray and squirts it over the floor outside the lift.

This had better work.

Rock charges towards the lift but slips and is sent sliding wildly across the room.

Squawk!

The lift doors close and Blue is safe for now.

Phew!

But when he gets out of the lift on Level 3, all the pigeons have already gone.

Oh coo ... what a stink! AND the pigeons have left with all the goo!

All except one.

Birdseed!

26

The roof of the goo factory slides open. As Birdseed flies out, his Stealth Hawk Security Team swoops down on Blue.

No worries. I'll use my turbo-charged rockets to out-fly them.

WHOOSH!

Blue escapes! Seconds later ...

KER BOOM

... Birdseed's volcano base erupts.

Blue's spy watch is working again. He quickly makes a call to Stella Bird at the office.

Birdseed's base has exploded! Birdseed has escaped and he has a squad of super-fit pigeons on its way to the Golden Feather Awards. We've got to stop them. They're going to drop super-smelly goo on all the film stars!

We can see the pigeons on radar, Blue. They're still 100 km from the target but moving fast. Any ideas?

Blue pecks some numbers into his spy watch.

Our ship, HMS *Magnetron*, is nearby. Get it to sail under the pigeons' flight path …

… then turn the ship's Mega Magnet on to full power. The super-smelly goo is in metal cans, strapped to the pigeons.

Stay on the phone, Blue, and we'll try it.

Birdseed's super-fit pigeons fly as hard as they can but the Mega Magnet on HMS *Magnetron* is too strong. One by one, the pigeons are pulled onto the deck of the ship.

All that training for nothing!

Don't worry. We're still going to be on TV. Smile!

A plot to goo film stars by super-baddie Birdseed has today caused a stink …

COO NEWS

BRAVO! Your plan worked. Well done, Agent Blue!

HOORAY!

Blue is back at the spy base. He's hoping for some peace and quiet so he can get some sleep. No such luck!

A new message flashes up on Blue's spy watch.

MAIL

Check **THIS** out, Agent Blue!

I'll be back ...

Birdseed

Blast!

THE END

Agent Blue
AND
THE SWIRLY WHIRLY

There are satellites in space, above Earth. Signals from satellites help people to watch TV and make phone calls.

2

... is sent to TVs here ...

A TV show from here ...

1

... here ...

... and here.

3

A boy in Singapore phones ...

4

... his Dad in Australia.

At the Pigeon Spy Agency, Chief Stella Bird isn't happy.

How many satellites are there above Earth, Agent Blue?

Thousands, Chief!

Well, all the TV satellites have disappeared. No more *Pop Pigeons* until we get them back.

Oh no!

You need to go to the Pigeon Space Station to find out what's going on … I suspect Birdseed is causing trouble again!

First, Blue tries scuba diving to get an idea of what it feels like to float in space.

Ever been scuba diving before, Blue?

No, Sir!

Next, Blue experiences what take-off will feel like.

Feeling a bit sick, Sir …

Don't mess up your spacesuit!

Professor Z and Astronaut Wing show Blue the controls on *Falcon 8*.

Press the Wallaby Warp Drive button to travel super-fast.

Why is it called that?

You travel super-fast but you bounce like a wallaby.

BOING BOING

Can you guess what the Hedgehog Defence Shield does?

Does it make *Falcon 8* all prickly?

Correct! And the Chameleon Cloaking Device makes *Falcon 8* look like ANYTHING you want!

Wing takes Blue to a special training room.

I'm going to show you how to do things while you are weightless.

WEIGHTLESS

First they practise eating while weightless …

I've never had to chase my beans before!

… then sleeping …

If I hang upside down I look like a bat!

… then having a wash …

No birdbaths … just a flannel? Can I bring my rubber duck?

… then exercising.

Why do we need to do two hours of exercise a day?

Being weightless weakens your muscles.

RRRRR!

RRRRRR!

Blue waits nervously to see if he has passed his training.

Well done, Blue. Training complete!

YOU'RE AN ASTRONAUT

The next day, Blue and Wing wait for blast-off. Chief calls Blue on the video-phone.

Good luck, Agent Blue. Remember, we need those satellites back!

Yes, Chief!

10 9 8 7 6 5 4 3 2 1

BLAST-OFF!

Blue's stomach flips. The force pins him to his seat and he can't move a feather.

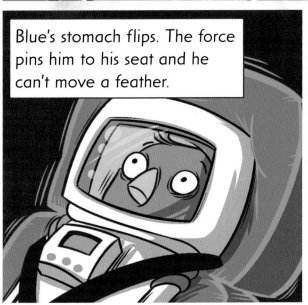

The rocket and shuttle separate.

Coo ... I'm in space!

Chief calls them again. Super-baddie, Birdseed, has sent the Pigeon Spy Agency a message.

It IS Birdseed stealing all the satellites!

But why would Birdseed want all the satellites, Chief?

We think he's …

CRACKLE FIZZ FIZZ...

The signal is lost.

Wing points out of the shuttle window.

Look!

The Pigeon Space Station! Hooray!

Yes, but what's that shadow behind it?

As they get closer, they can see the name 'Swirly Whirly' on the side of the strange shape.

SWIRLY WHIRLY

The Swirly Whirly thing is getting very close to the Pigeon Space Station ...

I don't like it, Wing. We have to stop it!

But it's too late. The Space Station is sucked into the Swirly Whirly.

THUNK!

Blue and Wing gasp in horror. Suddenly, a familiar voice booms out over the video-phone …

Who's a clever pigeon, then?

BIRDSEED!

We meet again, Agent Blue. Do you like my Swirly Whirly?

What IS that thing?

It's a remote-controlled super vacuum that sucks up anything that gets in its way!

Birdseed wins all the awards

BIRDSEED
BROADCASTING
COMPANY

Super Chef starring ME!
The news ... all about ME!
A chat show with ME
interviewing ME!
My name on EVERYTHING.
I'll be **FAMOUS**!

Swirly Whirly heads off into space looking for more satellites.

A minute later, Wing flies *Falcon 8* close to the mouth of Swirly Whirly.

Falcon 8 gets sucked inside the Swirly Whirly.

The hedgehog spikes stick into the sides of Swirly Whirly. Has the plan worked?

Swirly Whirly detects the blockage. It engages its reverse suction.

Blue and Wing have everything crossed.

Swirly Whirly's reverse suction tries to blow *Falcon 8* back out into space. It is super-powerful!

Let's hope the hedgehog spikes hold us in place!

Two hours later ... Swirly Whirly, with *Falcon 8* still stuck inside, reaches Birdseed's Space Base.

We're stopping, Blue. What do we do next?

Swirly Whirly lands. Wing turns off the Hedgehog Defence Shield and sets the Chameleon Cloaking Device to 'invisible'.

Blue and Wing jump out of *Falcon 8*. They creep through Swirly Whirly and into Birdseed's Space Base.

Wow! It's HUGE!

You stay here with *Falcon 8*, while I search for Birdseed.

But what if Blue doesn't come back? I'm going to follow him.

Blue isn't sure which way to go. But someone has been eating popcorn ... and they've been dropping bits.

Yum! I'll follow the popcorn trail. It must lead somewhere.

Mmm ... yum.

What's this up ahead?

Suddenly, Blue finds himself in a huge control room. He quickly hides but it's too late.

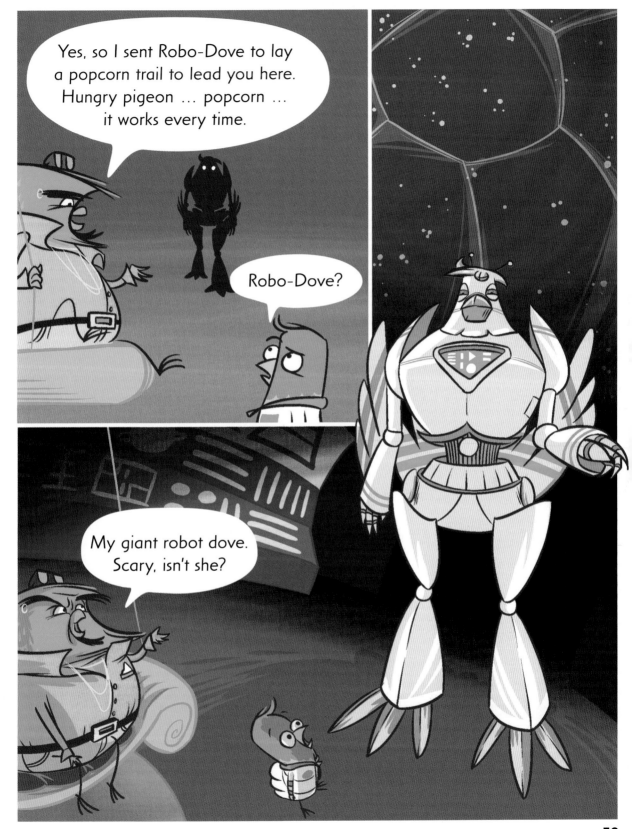

She doesn't scare ME, Birdseed!

We'll see about that! Robo-Dove ... GET HIM!

Robo-Dove's eyes light up and she charges at Blue.

Eeek!

Blue turns and flies away but Robo-Dove is fast. Her beak snaps at Blue's tail.

You can fly, Blue, but you can't hide.

Robo-Dove chases Blue around Birdseed's Space Base.
Just as Blue is about to lose his tail feathers ...

... someone grabs him and pulls him into a cupboard.

Wing! What are you doing here?

Saving you from Robo-Dove!

Even in the dark cupboard, Blue can see that Wing is smiling.

Birdseed STOLE Robo-Dove ...

Who from?

The Pigeon Space Station!

So ...?

On the count of three, they burst out of the cupboard.

Blue distracts Robo-Dove with some interesting dance moves ...

What about ballet? Do you know *Swan Lake*?

Like my funky chicken dance, Robo-Dove?

Whoop, whoop ... Birdman-style!

... while Wing plucks a feather from her wing.

65

Robo-Dove is so distracted, she doesn't even notice when Wing flies under her arm.

Tickle, tickle!

Robo-Dove falls to the floor, laughing.

Hee! Hee!

Quickly, Blue reaches under Robo-Dove's wing and presses the button.

CLICK WHIRRR PING!

Birdseed's the enemy. Blue is your friend.

Robo-Dove turns to Blue, smiling.

Horrible Birdseed.
Best friend Blue.

Coo … it worked, Wing!
But we still need to
stop Birdseed.

You think you can
stop me, Agent Blue?

Blast! Birdseed's
snuck up on us.

Robo-Dove, grab them and bring them to me!

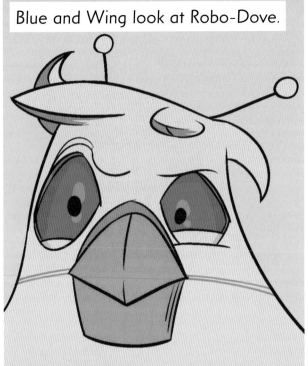

Blue and Wing look at Robo-Dove.

Uh oh. Something's wrong. Robo-Dove should be scaring Blue ... but she's scaring ME!

Big hug, Birdseed.

Birdseed can see the glint in Robo-Dove's eyes. She is planning to give him a VERY big hug indeed.

Argh ... I'm off! But don't get too comfortable, Agent Blue. I'll be back!

Birdseed runs away. Robo-Dove, Blue and Wing race after him.

They are too slow. Birdseed flies away in his escape pod … Robo-Dove chases after him.

Birdseed's getting away again!

Never mind. We have his Space Base and Swirly Whirly. We can catch him later.

WHOOMP
WHOOMP
WHOOMP

We need a plan to get the satellites back and working again.

We might even be home in time to watch *Pop Pigeons*!

Robo-Dove shows Blue and Wing how to operate the remote controls for Swirly Whirly. They fly Swirly Whirly back out into space and press the Reverse Suction button.

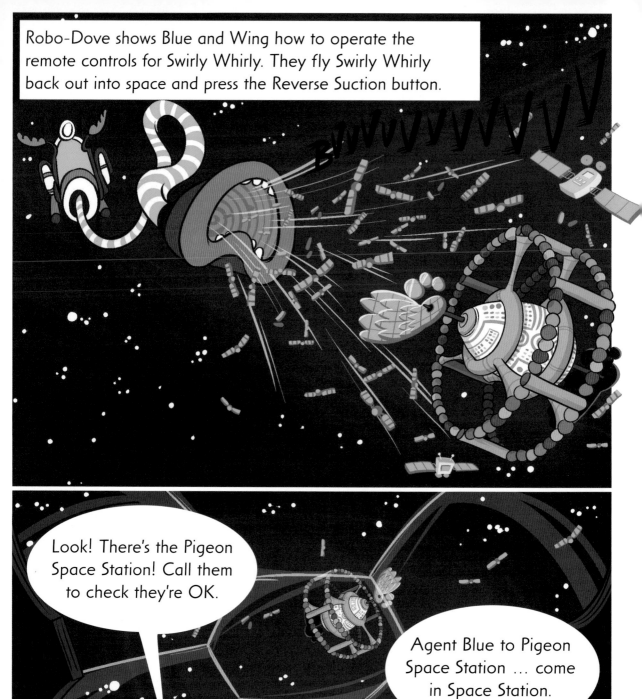

A few nervous seconds later …

This is Commander Beak at the Pigeon Space Station. Who am I talking to?

This is Astronaut Wing and Agent Blue. Are you all OK?

We're fine. Thank you for rescuing us. It was very dark and dusty in there!

Good to see you've rescued Robo-Dove, too!

Chirp!

One hour later ... Commander Beak arrives and takes control of Birdseed's Space Base and Swirly Whirly.

There will be no more mischief from Birdseed while I'm in charge!

Good to hear it, sir. What about Robo-Dove? Will she go back to the Pigeon Space Station?

I think she's earned herself a holiday first. Why don't you take her back to Earth with you on *Falcon 8*?

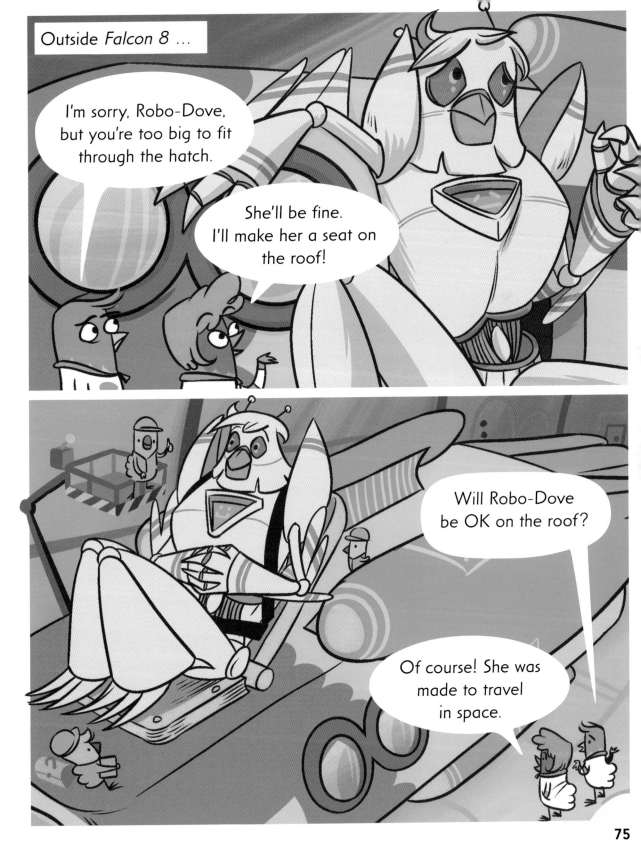

Robo-Dove has a brilliant time. It's like bouncing around on a giant trampoline!

Chief Stella Bird, Perch and Professor Z are waiting when they land.

Aah … THAT Robo-Dove. Excellent!

To celebrate their safe return, Chief invites everyone to her house to have tea and watch *Pop Pigeons*.

Two weeks later … Blue waves goodbye to Robo-Dove and Wing. They are heading back to the Pigeon Space Station.

Now for some peace and quiet …

Poor Blue. No chance! A new message flashes on his spy watch.

MAIL

Don't get too comfortable, Agent Blue.

I'll be back!

Birdseed

Blast!

THE END

After reading activities

Quick quiz

See how fast you can answer these questions! Look back at the stories if you can't remember.

1) In *Agent Blue and the Super-smelly Goo*, why does Stella choose Agent Blue for the mission against Birdseed?

2) What is Blue's undercover name on the mission against Birdseed?

3) Which awards ceremony is Birdseed planning to ruin?

4) In *Agent Blue and the Swirly Whirly*, why does Birdseed want to make a giant satellite?

5) What is the name of the space shuttle that Blue travels in?

6) How does Blue find the control room in Birdseed's Space Base?

Try this!

- What other animals might make good spies? Perhaps a very tiny animal who wouldn't be spotted? Or a clever animal who could pick up clues?

  - Think of your own new animal spy character. Draw a picture of them and give them a name. You could invent some cool gadgets for them too!

Answer: 1) Blue is new – and Birdseed would recognise all the other agents; **2)** Max Pond; **3)** the Golden Feather Awards; **4)** to blast Earth with 24-hour Birdseed TV; **5)** *Falcon 8*; **6)** by following a trail of popcorn.

OXFORD
UNIVERSITY PRESS

Great Clarendon Street, Oxford, OX2 6DP, United Kingdom

Oxford University Press is a department of the University
of Oxford. It furthers the University's objective of excellence
in research, scholarship, and education by publishing
worldwide. Oxford is a registered trade mark of Oxford
University Press in the UK and in certain other countries

First published 2015
This edition published 2019

British Library Cataloguing in Publication Data
Data available

ISBN: 978-0-19-276979-4

10 9 8 7 6 5 4 3 2 1

Paper used in the production of this book is a natural, recyclable product
made from wood grown in sustainable forests. The manufacturing process
conforms to the environmental regulations of the country of origin.

Printed in China

Acknowledgements
Series Advisor: Nikki Gamble
Illustrated by Rebecca Clements
Designed by Oxford University Press in collaboration with Miranda Costa